TANTRIC SEX:

THE ULTIMATE GUIDE TO MASTER THE ART OF TANTRIC SEX

JOANNE BENNET

BOOK 2 : TANTRIC SEX POSITIONS

Introduction to Tantric Sex Positions

Tantric Sex or Neotantra is essentially spiritual sex. It takes the old beliefs and teachings of Tantra. It brings them into our modern relationships and sex lives to help us better connect in our romantic relationships and to be one with our bodies and sensations. Tantric Sex is about an exchange of energy between partners and getting in touch with the feelings of our body. It is also about removing distractions and being mindful to have more intense, longer-lasting, full-body orgasms.

Tantric sex takes the theories of the Tantra for the male and female pleasure and uses them with sex. Sex with oneself or sex with a partner is done through a deep connection. You practice being connected to yourself and your deeper feelings to feel your feelings and reach orgasm quicker and with more intensity more easily. Tantric sex is so useful for couples, especially those who have been together for some time. At the beginning of your relationship, you were connected by the lust, the exploration of each other and the excitement. Now, since you know each other so well it can be hard to reach that same feeling of discovery with them. Tantric sex can help you get there.

Examples of How to Practice It

Some couples who have been practicing tantra together for quite a while have reached a point where they can come together in a hug or some other embraces. After about a minute, they can both orgasm without ever touching their own or the other person's genitals! They even do this fully clothed. This shows you the power that Tantra can have. While this isn't always practiced to reach an orgasm, sometimes it can happen through getting deeply in touch with your body. Of course, if you are just beginning your practice of Tantric Sex, this is not the expectation, but over time this may be something you wish to strive for.

To begin practicing Tantra and noticing the changes it will bring, you can do many different things as long as the intention and the method is the same. You can do things like giving each other massages (either in the erogenous zones or otherwise), you can bathe or shower together or you can sit or stand in a tight embrace. The point is that you are connecting on a deep level through mindfulness and a deep connection of your bodies and sensations. The beautiful thing about Tantra is that it is focused on the couple and reaching orgasm together. This is great for our purposes as this will help you to share your orgasm with your partner which will lead to an increase in intimacy. We will look at more examples of how to practice this type of sex and emotional connection below.

Through Tantric Edging

Using Tantric Edging is a sure way to make sure that your orgasms not only last longer, but also that they become much more intense than ever before!

Edging is a technique in Tantric Sex that involves being so in tune with your body and its sensations that you can reach the point of orgasm but stop yourself from actually reaching orgasm. Doing this a few times in a single session before letting yourself reach orgasm finally, will make for an unbelievably more intense orgasm than ever before. This will provide you with a much deeper orgasm than you would have had if you had just let yourself have the orgasm the first time. As we explained earlier, Tantric Sex involves spirituality and being in tune with the sensations and feelings within your body. Becoming better at this type of practice as you go about your everyday life, while also including some of this practice to your sex life, will allow you to be better able to feel and understand what you are feeling and what it means. In this case, it will allow you to feel when you are about to orgasm, and thus, how to hold off that orgasm until later.

It is a good idea to practice this technique during masturbation in the beginning stages, because having a partner there with you may make you unable to control your orgasm, which may mean that you are unable to stop yourself from coming and then you will be unable to practice edging. Once you master this technique on your own, however, taking it to the bedroom with a partner will make it that much more exciting and pleasurable for both of you. If you cannot control your orgasms on your own yet, you will have trouble trying to control them with your sexy and seductive partner right in front of you, tempting you!

To practice this during masturbation, begin touching yourself however you please, and let your pleasure build. When your sensations reach a high point, let them flood your body, almost as if you are going to come but hold yourself back from actually reaching that orgasm. To do this, stop touching yourself and take a breath or two, whatever helps you to hold it back. When you have felt these sensations but successfully held off your explosion of pleasure, begin touching yourself again and bring yourself to the edge of orgasm once again but do not let yourself get there just yet. Continue to do this over and over a few more times until you have built up such intense pleasure that you cannot hold off any longer. Begin touching yourself once again and bring your body back to the edge of that same orgasm. Still, this time keep going with these feelings of pleasure until you finally allow yourself to orgasm and feel your body have the most intense, mind-blowing release of pleasure of your entire life.

Through Tantric Massages

A Yoni Massage is a vaginal massage that is intended to open up the woman to her sexuality, her pleasure, and her sexual desires. As a partner, you can perform this type of massage for your woman to unlock her repressed sexual energy and help her to get in touch with it.

This can be done in a variety of ways, but the position we are going to discuss is a Yoni Massage. Begin by setting the ambiance, either in the bathroom with a bathtub, or in the bedroom. Set up some candles, some flowers, or anything that will make the surroundings relaxing and calm. Begin by having her breathe deeply and focus on her body and its sensations. You can get into the bed with her for added intimacy. Begin by slowly and gently massaging around her entire vulva and her clitoral area. The key to this type of massage is to do everything very slowly. Begin to massage her clitoris slowly and not to make her come. When ready, and with lots of waterproof lube, slide one finger inside of her vagina and gently begin massaging the upper wall. Here is where her G-spot is located. Encourage her to express and release any sounds she naturally makes. Move your finger in a circular motion slowly and with your other hand, massage her pelvic area and clitoris. This connects the inner with the outer. Continue to do this and let the experience unfold with no end goal in mind. If she reaches orgasm, she can do so, but if she doesn't, she can just enjoy the pleasures that she is getting from your massage. As explained earlier, this massage is intended to reconnect a woman with her pleasure and allow her to focus on herself and her body. After this massage, she will feel more in touch with her body. If penetrative sex ensues, both of you will feel even more pleasure and intensity of orgasms because of how engorged and activated her vagina and clitoris will be.

Description of Tantric Sex

What is Tantric Sex?

Tantric sex has increased a great deal of fame in the ongoing past. It has gotten well in the western world with a ton of famous people like Sting, Madonna, and even the late Steve Jobs. They had confessed to having attempted this strategy. Presently, it has gradually discovered acknowledgment everywhere throughout the world. A few idealists do have confidence in their adequacy in accomplishing more prominent delight.

Tantric sex fulfills individuals truly, intellectually, and profoundly also. Tantric sex gives total fulfillment and causes the whole body to feel amazingly pleasurable, helps in sincerely associating with one's accomplice, and on an otherworldly level; it helps in the amalgamation of two spirits and carries them closer to divine nature.

Tantra utilizes two energies: the female and the male energies. The female vitality is alluded to as Shakti, and the male vitality is as Shiva. Shakti and Shiva are Hindu divine beings, and their object of worship adore includes the revering of Ling and Yon. Linga implies the penis and far off methods the vagina. At the point when a couple takes part in tantric sex, at that point, the female vitality present in the body, Shakti, ascends through the various chakras. It punctures through the female community that is alluded to as the Kundalini. Afterward, it converges with the male vitality, alluded to as Shiva. This combination of energies helps in framing a bond that outperforms the human domain.

Different Parts of Tantric Sex

There are three significant primary parts of Tantric sex, and these are tantric correspondence, tantric positions, and tantric working out. Tantric correspondence is a procedure that helps in the converging of a couple sincerely and intellectually. This aide in bringing them near each other and is equipped for transforming an average couple into perfect partners. Tantric positions are sure places that will help in uniting a couple explicitly. There are diverse tantric activities just as breathing strategies that will help in harvesting the most out of tantric sex. More data about these three parts of Tantric sex has been clarified in the next parts.

Tantric sex helps in liberating the body, brain, and soul. This is conceivable through the act of the strategies, as referenced before. Quieting one's brain is a vital part of any training that includes reflection. Fundamentally, for rehearsing tantric sex, it is necessary to facilitate your brain. These strategies have been referenced in the book.

In contrast to customary sex, the lessons of tantric sex focus on making the members mindful of their activities while engaged with a sexual demonstration with their accomplice. If you are aware of your activities, at that point, you can guarantee that you can actuate a sentiment of worship and even regard for your accomplice. It is tied in with regarding your body and that of your accomplice's too. The essential target of tantric sex is to assist you with loosening up your body and brain. At the point when you can discover this discharge, you will have the option to communicate without any difficulty that will develop and reinforce the security that exists among you and your accomplice, the sort of adoration that would bind together your spirits.

Tantric sex is, without a doubt, mysterious. You will find that the different strategies that have been referenced in this guidebook will not just assistance you in relinquishing your feelings of trepidation and hurt. However, they will likewise help you in communicating better. Likewise, as an additional advantage, these methods will help you in feeling more youthful and increasingly loose.

Why you need to try Tantric Sex?

It can help in recuperating you

Customary sex has the limit concerning fulfilling your physical needs and inclinations. Yet, Tantric sex can help in fulfilling your enthusiastic needs too. All the horrible encounters that you may have suffered before, your feelings of dread and weaknesses that you have should be possible away with the utilization of Tantric sex. Tantric sex makes utilization of various meditational methods centers around your breathing and keeping in touch with your accomplice and doing other easily overlooked details that will improve sex such a vast amount than it at any point was.

This will likewise help in accomplishing a more beneficial and more joyful condition. The delicate contacts of Tantric sex will help in shaping a more grounded bond with your accomplice and wash away the entirety of your terrible feelings and encounters.

Accomplishing full-body climaxes

A full-body climax may appear to be fascinating and questionable simultaneously. Tantric sex will assist you with accomplishing this. The delight that you can be understanding while at the same time, taking part in Tantric sex is higher than average sex. The explanation behind this is, when drilled appropriately, it can, without a doubt, help in accomplishing a full-body climax, and this is very regular. This happens when you begin concentrating on spreading the lethargic sexual vitality that is available in your body to all the cells in the body rather than inherently limiting it to your privates. This will heighten the delight you are encountering and make your body wake up.

It very well may be testing

Tantric sex is not, in every case, simple to perform. Whether or not or not, you have in your accomplice for your entire life, it can, in any case, be very testing. You will require somewhat more concentration and practice to get the hang of tantric sex. Tantric sex is a perfect type of lovemaking. To appreciate every one of its advantages, it is significant that the individuals who are taking part in it can relinquish every one of their hindrances completely. There is not a fast or a simple manner by which you will have the option to get its hang. You should relinquish all the past ideas of lovemaking that you may have had and rethink this whole procedure. You can begin by sitting on the bed or any agreeable surface and look into one another's eyes. It is tied in with framing a bond with your accomplice and keeping up an association with your accomplice, all through the length of sex.

There are Tantric sex courses accessible also. Before you misunderstand any thoughts, these courses are not bunched bashes, nor do they incorporate any realistic exhibits. These are classes that will show a couple to associate with one another on a more profound level and help in shaping a bond that rises above world. Different points are shrouded in these courses, and these can be rehearsed with your accomplice inside the holiness and protection of your home. There are online courses accessible too. When you have the hang of the nuts and bolts, you can take part in some staggering sex.

Tantric sex mends you
Maybe one of the best potential employments of tantric sex is that it can help in mending your body and soul. It will likewise assist you with letting go of undesirable considerations and cause your brain to feel lighter. You may have been harmed before or might have persevered through some type of dismissal in your past connections. Tantric sex will help you in pardoning yourself. It will assist you with learning to adore yourself indeed and to esteem your body as you were intended to. Various methods have

been referenced in this guidebook that will help you in recuperating and liberating yourself from any blame or injury that you may have persevered. You will see that you will feel progressively engaged if you follow the guidance that has been given in this guidebook. Tantric sex will, without a doubt, assist you with mending, and it is done through the accompanying advances. You should recognize the episode that has harmed you before. This hurt could have been genuine or fanciful. Along these lines, the following stage is to decide if it was genuine or nonexistent. Sexual incitement will help you in recognizing the distinction. You will have the option to locate the negative feelings appended to this specific damage and can release them. Supplant these negative sentiments with positive feelings and encounters that will enable you to recuperate.

The Science Behind Tantric Sex

In Tantric Sex, everything comes down to the belief that women are generally taught to always focus on the needs of others and on taking care of others, as well as to place more importance on the pleasure of others than on themselves. It is believed that women are so disconnected from their feelings and sensations that they must begin a practice of mindfulness to reconnect with their feelings and sensations.

Tantric Theory states that women have a more difficult time than men when it comes to reaching orgasm. Specifically, it states that women are quite preoccupied with the duties of the household, including the children and their needs, the household and its needs, their work, their friends, and anything and anyone else in their lives. They are also preoccupied with subtle distractions such as noises or the temperature, demonstrating that they are always on high alert to ensure everything is running smoothly and that nobody is uncomfortable in any way. This is like what we tackled when we looked at how to get in the right mindset for sex in terms of removing distractions and prioritizing foreplay.

In short, Tantric theory believes that women are raised to focus on the pleasure and wellbeing of others and are as a result, out of touch entirely with their bodies, their pleasure, and their desires (these desires can be both of a sexual nature and otherwise, but here, we will focus on the sexual desires). Because of this, when it comes to sex, women tend to be unable to put aside their focus on others and turn that focus inward to themselves. When in a long-term relationship, they will be so invested in the pleasure of their partner that they will not focus on their own. Even in a casual sexual encounter, the woman will be focused on ensuring that she is giving the man a good time at the expense of her pleasure.

To further its theories on the attention of women and their focus on many outside factors during sex, Tantric theory states that even if she wanted to, she would not have the ability to turn her focus inward. The belief is that women are unable to get in touch with the sensations of their body or their sexual desires because they have been raised always to put those aside, thus never developing the skills to do so. If she is not able to get in touch with these parts of herself, she will have great difficulty reaching orgasm. This is because she will have difficulty feeling what she is feeling, what she likes and doesn't like, and what she wants her partner to do to give her an orgasm. She will likely even have difficulty reaching orgasm when she is alone for the same reasons.

Tantric theory also has a theory concerning men and their pleasure. It is believed that men generally have short and intense orgasms and that it is possible for them to have better and longer-lasting orgasms through the practice of mindfulness as well. Tantra focuses on teaching men to be able to prolong their orgasms and make them more all-encompassing as well as to extend their pleasure overall.

Tantric sex has many techniques and methods for overcoming these challenges, and its primary intention concerning women is to help them refocus their attention to themselves and their body's sensations. By refocusing on their bodies, it allows women to fully access the parts of their brain related to sexual arousal without just as equally activating the parts of their brain related to worry and concern for others.

The practice of Tantra, in general, involves being in touch with one's feelings and one's breath- almost like a meditation. Neotantra or Tantric Sex takes this idea and uses it concerning sex. Sex with oneself or sex with a partner is done through a deep connection to oneself and one's partner. To do this, you practice being connected to yourself and your deeper feelings to feel all of the sensations in your body more quickly and reach orgasm quicker and with more intensity.

Tantric sex is so useful for couples, especially those who have been together for some time. At the beginning of your relationship, you were connected by the lust, the exploration of each other, and the excitement. Now, since you know each other so well, it can be hard to reach that same feeling of discovery in the bedroom. Tantric sex can help you get there.

For men, Tantric Sex aims to help them to feel and enjoy their orgasms fully, to make them more intense and longer lasting and to make them build up much more before releasing. It teaches women to be more present in their pleasure and as a result, their orgasms. Accomplishing these things as well as reaching a higher level of intimacy with your partner is sure to bring you to a new level of connection within your relationship, no matter how long you have been together. Devote yourselves to this practice over time (it will not happen overnight), and it will give you something to work towards as a couple and get you excited about sex with each other again.

Basic Tantric Sexuality Reflections and Knowledge

There are scarcely any areas where there are more strange religious beliefs and prohibitions than sexuality. Why is this so? So that you can get rid of all the superstition about sexuality that prevails in our society, I invite you to first go to the scientific level of physics:

Sexuality is Touch.

Colloquially it is spoken, one would touch the other - BUT - and this is already the first and most important finding that supplies us with the physics: If we enlarge the skin with an electron microscope, where this alleged contact takes place, then we see that there no contact exists at all. If you increase the atom at this point to apple size, then these atoms are far more than 20 kilometers apart. From touch also far and wide no trace. On the contrary. The atom, that is, the matter of our body touch, is not in sexual contamination. Here the physics is reduced to a sober, clear, and factually founded view, namely, that we must do in the process of touch, even during sex, with a pure fusion and exchange of energies. Our material bodies do not touch at all. We do not feel the other's body, but its energy field. We also experience a pure energy event!

18

Sex is an Energy Event

And from the moment we are aware of this truth, that we are dealing with an energy event, with an energetic event, we can also ask the right questions to improve further and consecrate our lives. If we believe, sexuality has something to do with touch, because then we get stuck on the material plane. Only when we realize that a touch is an interaction between the two partners, we can ask ourselves questions about how this energy-fusion process can be influenced, how it works, what sense it has, how it can be improved, what it does, how it can help us achieve a better quality of life, how it can be used to separate from illnesses and much more.

Thought models to explain the world. It is always that a model is so useful, the more it corresponds to reality. According to the old model, sexuality is the belief that you are touching the body on a physical level, it has the purpose of having children and reproducing.

In Tantra, however, a model is used that is closer to reality because here are the findings that the interaction takes place not on a material-physical, but the energy level. Only then can the fusion on the energy level, meaning what sex is, can be consciously understood, practiced, and used, for example, for healing, soul growth, and the manifestation of life goals and desires. (With the specific world view or model about the sexuality of man, all this is not possible.) So, for example, are feelings that flow in the body or the aura of man. The Tantric knowledge implies that these sensory energies depend on specific energy flow laws that not only depend on the healing quality of your sex life but even your entire life. Only when the man has known and understood this new model, this tantric knowledge, is he no longer subject to the limited ancient beliefs about sexuality. He can now take advantage of the possibilities of sexuality, the possibilities of curing disease, to the universal creation of energy fields, and creative energies for the benefit of his life. It opens a whole new world of fantastic unlimited possibilities to heal one's life and life together, to the creation of all that is conceivable. When two people are tantrically united in love, their potential for creation is immeasurable. The limitations are only the not yet released blockages of the two partners. Only then can one realize how incredibly primitive the old belief is that sexuality would only serve to procreate. But then one can also recognize why certain religious power-oriented circles have even implanted all these limited views on sexuality in the people because gods are bad to rule. For these circles, sex and contact bans are of fundamental importance. Their empire of power, created energetically from occult sacrificial and lodge ritual energies, cannot resist an energy-pure formation of love energy as it can arise through tantric love. By contrast, healthy sex cannot produce such an energetically stable entity on the mental level. This is not possible, even if the love of two people is continuously on and on and leads to continuous energy loss.

Right and Wrong Sex

Right and wrong sex - that sounds very provocative at first. 99% of all people must look like a healthy sexuality that is in the flow of the Divine Life, the Living One. There are far too many bans on thinking in our religious society about sexuality and the connection to God and the sacred to the purpose of life, which is used anyway. The religions have made men the victim of their sexual beliefs and doctrines. I would like to define it this way: Proper sex increases the human energy level, wrong sex does not. First,

Why is the energy level so fundamentally important?
We need energy for our mission in life, to fulfill that indeed consists of developing ourselves. We are creator gods, but still, this creation process needs energy. And by that, I do not mean the birth of a child, but the birth of all your goals and desires into the reality of your life. All this need are creation energies, and of course, the higher our energy level of these subtle energies, the more comfortable and the more our desires can be fulfilled, the better our lives will be. Thus, sexuality, in a holistic way becomes

a higher quality of life for the two tantra partners in all areas of life. And yes, of course, this also applies to the healing processes that require just as much subtle energy for them to take place at all. When someone starts tantra, the body often starts healing processes that have been going on for years. Still, for which people did not have enough energy before, so they could not run out earlier.

What is "wrong sex"?

Wrong sex is also a sexuality that does not lead to more energy. It is based on wrong beliefs, so to speak on the wrong belief. What is based on lies does not lead to the divine and that the sexuality does not lead to the divine, is, of course, already the first religious faith lie must be overcome?

Proper sex is a sexuality that helps people.

When we realize that this is about energies, about the exchange of energies, also about the TILES of energies. The flow of energy is the alpha and omega of healthy sexuality. Everything can be measured in the flow of energy; it is the most crucial measure of the quality of any sexual interaction.

The energy flow is the quality of our life messenger.

The less energy flow blocks the human carries within him, the closer his consciousness is to the divine. And the sense of the divine approach is, of course, the meaning of sexuality.

Old Thought Patterns About Sexuality

Belief, women or the female is worthless than the male

Generalized, one can summarize the most blatant of all ancient thought patterns is the belief that yin is less valuable than yang. That the female is more worthless than the male. That feelings are worth less than logical thoughts. The Yin and the Yang are simply only two directions of the same size, if from the zero-point field (that is, from the god). It is always the case that yin and yang are the same sizes, so equivalent. A mountain is always as high as the valley is deep. And the valley is as deep as the mountain is high. Both are inseparable, though sometimes it may seem as if we can look at them one at a time. And only when the yin and yang reunite to return in unity, balance the mountain and the valley again, allowing the mountain and the valley to be one unit when the yin and yang vibration returns balance to zero, so again to the zero point field, then something new, the creation goes on. But this concerns every creative field, not just the procreation of a child.

The belief that the purpose of sexuality is to have children

To understand, and on a deep level, that sexuality serves not only to make children but to the contrary, that the fusion of Yin and Yang energies forms the basis of absolutely every creative process, is a rethinking of another widespread belief pattern by 180 degrees. The superstition, so to speak, of our time, is to believe that sex is only for children. The exact opposite is the case! There are an incredible number of extraterrestrial civilizations where having children is completely devoid of sexuality, that alone should make us think. Is that what sexual interactions are capable when, when the normality in the universe is entirely different?

There is nothing without meaning in this universe. If the man can produce sexual energies, then that must make sense. Or, conversely, when someone is incarnated in a human body, then his soul becomes evident that man learns and practices to deal with sexual energies and feelings. This is logical because otherwise, we could have bodies that can do without sexual acts, which, as I said in the universe, is the normality. Why do we have a male or female body?

To learn, to practice, to understand sexuality.

Central Theme of Human Sexuality

It is about the fusion of Yin and Yang energies, which forms the basis of every creative process. We also learn how to deal with the energies here and then serve us as a foundation and understanding for the entire cosmos. You cannot ascend to intergalactic consciousness without mastering these things. Therefore, planet earth is also relatively isolated from the rest of the universe; at least we humans are not allowed to possess UFOs, quite obviously because we are not yet mature enough for the vast world of adults. The people are little minds who have not met everyone yet.

The Tantra of Love

Most of the tantric texts agree that love is one of the most fundamental and energetic forces a human being can encounter. That force can be used positively to progress one's spiritual experience. They say that the love we can feel for another human being is but a tiny part of the love we can feel for God and that sex is a physical manifestation of that love. They feel that sex when enjoyed with the right focus is a powerful tool, and one that can be used with God's blessing.

It may seem strange to Westerners that sex can be enjoyed freely and yet still be part of a spiritual or religious life. This approach is somewhat different from Western religions where sex is often seen as something to be repressed or denied.

The Chakras

The tantric texts agree that there is a movement of energy within the human body during sex that can be both felt and used. This energy is physical. It rises during the arousal of sex and can be directed and channeled. According to the Hindu tantric texts we have within us six energy centers known as chakras. These energy centers each have a specific area of human life that they are said to control.

- The base chakra - Muladhara - is situated at the base of the spine between the genitals and the anus. This chakra governs our instincts and genetic coding. It is usually represented by a yellow square. The mantra for the base chakra is lam.

- The pelvic chakra - Swadhishthana - is situated at the genitals themselves. This chakra governs our sexual life. It is usually represented by a white crescent. The mantra for the pelvis chakra is vam.

- The navel chakra - Manipuraka - is situated at the navel. This chakra governs our power. It is usually represented by a red triangle. The mantra for the navel chakra is ram.

- The heart chakra - Anahata - is situated at the heart. This chakra governs our love. It is usually represented by a blue hexagon. The mantra for the heart chakra is yam.

- The throat chakra - Vishuddha - is situated at the throat. This chakra governs our communication. It is usually represented by a white circle. The mantra for the throat chakra is ham.

- The brow chakra - Ajna - is situated between the brows. This chakra governs our intellect and thought processes. It is usually represented by an inverted white triangle. The mantra for the brow chakra is om.

Each of these chakras also has a Hindu god attributed to it as well as various symbolic animals, flowers, elements, seasons and a letter of the Sanskrit alphabet. We need only be concerned with the basics in this guidebook.

The Crown Chakra

There is also another chakra worth considering; this is not a true chakra like the others but rather is known as a shuddha and it is situated at the crown of the head. It is sometimes known as the crown chakra, but it doesn't operate in quite the same way as the others. Its name is sahasrara and it is the home of the Goddess Shakti - the God Shiva is said to reside in the brow chakra. The whole point of raising the kundalini energy from the base chakra up the spine to the brow chakra, and then on the crown chakra, is to free Shiva so he may be reunited with Shakti. The great cosmic reunion of the male and female principles can take place. This state of divine bliss is known as samadhi - enlightenment.

Exercise 1

For the man

You should lie down somewhere warm and comfortable. Imagine the site of each chakra as a small tightly furled flower or small leather bag. As you breathe out make the mantra sound for each chakra as you visualize it in turn, starting with the base chakra and finishing with the brow chakra. Imagine each chakra to be a flower opening as you breathe out - or the small leather bag having drawn strings which are being slowly loosened.

Work your way up your body imagining each chakra opening as you make the mantra sound as you exhale. You need to do this exercise with your eyes closed so you can visualize each chakra in turn. This exercise can be done before you make love with your partner so that you are fully open and ready to feel energy moving within your body.

For the woman
You should lie down somewhere warm and comfortable. Imagine each chakra as a flower turned upside down. As you breathe out make the sound of the chakra mantra and imagine each chakra in turn, starting with the base chakra and finishing with the crown chakra, to be the flower slowly turning until it is upright. As it does so, imagine it becoming cooler and stiller as if filled with cold refreshing energy.

You should do this exercise before making love with your partner so that your chakras are open, and you are ready to feel the energy moving within your body.

Purifying energy

You can both also do this exercise as a method of cleansing or purifying your energy. As you visualize your energy reaching the crown chakra imagine it pouring out of the top of your head and being replaced with fresh new energy from your base chakra. Imagine all the collected energy of all your past lovers being replaced so that you can begin again with a fresh supply.

Exercise 2

Tantric Yoga Relaxation Position

Imuladhara sadhana

Both you and your lover lie downside by side on your backs but facing opposite ways - your feet to your lover's head and vice versa. The man should lie with the woman along his right side so he can place his right hand lightly across her vulva. The woman can then use her right hand to hold his penis lightly.

This is an exercise to feel the energy rising from the base chakra up through the pelvic chakra and beyond. Try to feel the warmth your lover's hand generates in and through your genitals. As the warmth spreads, focus on it and feel it spreading upwards as energy. The man will feel this energy slowly working its way up his spine, while for the woman the energy will rise slowly up through her belly first and then her breasts. The man's energy, being hotter and more volatile, may well rise faster but he should not rush it. The woman's energy, being cooler and slower to arouse, will take longer. If during this exercise either becomes aroused to the point of orgasm then that's all right. Because we are orgasm-oriented in the west it may take a while to learn to focus on the energy rather than the sexual/spiritual experience. Whatever way you do it, it should be an enjoyable experience. The whole basis of raising the kundalini energy is to share and experience the 'godhead'. If this is not done in a spirit of delight and enjoyment it will not be successful. Some have spent a whole lifetime practicing tantric sex and getting nowhere because they do the whole thing as a ritual and miss the point completely.

Arousal and enjoyment

You must enter into tantric sex with an approach of delight - what happens is happening and it's all right. Sometimes there will be a union of soul with soul and sometimes not - but the journey should be enjoyed without thought of the destination, or the experience that is presented along the way will be lost.

If, during exercise 2, you become aroused, enjoy it. And there should be no spiritual ego to taunt your partner with: 'oh, I attained enlightenment and all you achieved was orgasm'.

Using the kundalini energy

Use the experience as it comes and try to use the energy beneficially. The principal aim or objective of raising the kundalini energy is to reunite or connect with the energy of the universe through the unique and wonderful experience of sex. Tantra is a reunion with god.

The Three Forms of Energy

During exercise 3 the energy may become very sleepy - go with it and use the time given as a meditation. Focus on the brow chakra and allow yourself to appreciate what you can see, feel and hear. There is a reason, according to the tantric Buddhists, why the energy can take anyone of many different forms. It may be orgasmic, meditative or spiritually enlightening - it may even be all three - but the energy generated is being transformed into exactly what you need at any given moment. It may not be what you expect or even what you particularly want, but it will be what you need. The tantric Buddhists recommend that you go with it; if you do not fight the universe it will provide you with everything you need.

Being In Touch With Your Body

Exercise 3 will put you in touch with your genital feelings. We focus on our genitals usually only in the rush of orgasm or if they are being caressed. During this exercise you can focus on both yours and your partner's genitals. How do they feel? Wholesome and healthy? Or is there some residue guilt or inhibition there? According to the tantric Buddhists one of the reasons we sometimes fail to achieve a truly deep spiritual/sexual experience is because we are somehow hanging on to our fears and repression. During Exercise 3 you can explore your feelings about your sexuality - and your body as a sexual instrument.

Exercise 3

Chakra Sex Position

The man should sit on the floor and the woman should straddle him. He should insert his erect penis into her vulva, but neither should move. If the woman grasps the man around his back and he holds her around her shoulders, both should be able to relax and feel comfortable. Look into each other's eyes. The tantric texts suggest that you should both keep your tongue on the roof of your mouth as this helps the energy complete its circuit around your body. You should both feel the warmth coming from each other's pelvic chakra and concentrate on feeling the energy rising.

The Ceremony Behind Tantric Sex

Up until now in your life, you have probably just jumped into bed with your partner when the mood hit you, and there was no real ceremony of sex. It was simply something that resulted from feeling horny. Well, when you start to look at how Tantric Sex works, you will see that there is a lot more ceremony attached to it than simply jumping into bed. This celebration and preparation are vital because going into a relationship this close takes understanding by both of you. Thus, you should talk to your partner about what you want to achieve and make sure your partner is fully on board and prepared to experience what you will experience! Let me try and describe it to you so that you can persuade your partner a little about the benefits of Tantric Sex.

The sexual act is not just about orgasm. It is about putting your energy into your partner while your partner puts his/her energy into you. The combination of these energies is what makes the sexual arousal and eventual orgasm so intense. You may not have experienced this intensity before, and your partner may not have. An orgasm can be made to last. You will learn about extended bliss, and you will gain a better control of your orgasm. It will not be hit and miss anymore, and your partner will not feel that you came too early for them to feel fully satisfied. Being honest about what happens in everyday life will help as well. For example, it is not uncommon for a woman to fake her orgasm. The reason women do that is because they want their partner to feel like they did a good job and they are satisfied, but they are not!

Well, the anatomy is not as straightforward in a woman as it is in a man! You can see a penis on a man, but you cannot see a G-spot on a woman. Men sometimes do not get it. They do not understand where the G-spot is and most fumble at trying to find the clitoris. Tantric massage will allow full exploration of the body so that the two lovers are made more aware of their energy flow and will learn exactly which areas of the body give the most pleasure. The ceremony of tantric sex explores, and both parties learn each other's pleasure points and can control how long the orgasm lasts. That is a pretty powerful incentive for talking your partner into trying something new.

Ceremonial Rituals

Since this is something more spiritual than sexual, you may want to prepare your location for the occasion. You can do this anywhere, but we will start in the master bedroom. You will be using hot oils for the massage, so perhaps you will have to protect the bed with towels so that your sheets do not get stained. Start by dimming the lights or perchance turning them off completely, but before that, carefully and strategically place around the bedroom several glowing candles so you both can gain a glimpse of each other's glistening silhouette in the shimmering light. You can also prepare the atmosphere of the room with a scented diffuser if you are using unscented candles. Others will prefer the sounds of soft love songs quietly in the background. Still, Tantra prefers complete silence and concentration of each other's breathing. Do not forget that scent arouses one of your sexual pleasures!

During lovemaking, you may tend to try to extend activity so that you can climax after a given period. You need to understand that Tantric sex is about control in a very different way. It is surrender. It has nothing to do with tensing up. That is why the ceremony that leads up to ecstasy should be carried out in an atmosphere that encourages love to flow freely and privately. Your chants and moans of lovemaking should not be confined, and the release of energy from your Chakras should flow freely. By having ambiance in the room, and not bright lights, you're not forced to feel conscious about yourself. You can purely concentrate on what's happening to you just as your partner can surrender to what you are doing to them. That is why the preparation is so important. You will need to warm up the massage oils and make sure it is not too hot. You might also have some soft feathers to brush against the skin. Proper preparation of the location where the Tantric Sexual Ceremony will take place and the level of mastery of the Chakras' of the couple involved, measures up to complete ecstasy and wonderment!

You must be thoroughly clean. Think of what we explained before. The massage is a spiritual experience, and you must think of your partner's body differently. It is not about lustful feelings but is about adoration. That mutual love will take you beyond the ordinary touching, and there will not be areas of the body that are "no go" areas. Thus, cleanliness is vital as well as being scented in an unobtrusive way. For example, if you find your partner's perfume interferes with your concentration, then try using natural body scents, or herbal massage oils instead of preparing yourself with heavily commercial scented fragrances.

The ceremony of Tantric sex is a sacred one so you will need to switch off all outside interferences to apply yourself 100% to your partner's needs.

This ceremony means total surrender to each other. Thus, you need to switch off all outside interference and make sure that the time you choose to devote to each other is a time when there will be no interruption or distraction. Those who have children may need to find a time when the kids are not home as any distractions will take away from the Tantric sexual concentration and may make blockages of Chakras necessary to experience mind-blowing ecstasy. If you are worried about someone coming to the door, close your blinds, turn off the outside light and shut off your cell phones.

The adoration of the body and every part of the body – the connection of two souls and the ability to look each other in the eye while experiencing out-of-this-world sex are all part and parcel of the Tantric experience. This means you both need to want this. When you feel that is what you want as a couple, the ceremony and preparation are worth every bit of thought, and energy you put into it.

Tantra Lifestyle

One must understand that in the path to finding a "true tantra soulmate", love has to come from within. This simply means that you cannot truly be with a partner if you do not appreciate yourself. First things first, you need to fall in love with yourself before you can fall in love with another. Many people easily get depressed in their love relationship and they often find themselves in conflict with their partner because they feel a sense of unworthiness within themselves. Look at it this way, some people try to depend on others for their happiness. You would hear them often say that they are looking for their "better half" or that they need someone who would complete them. Some even believe that their lives can make no meaning until their "better half" comes into the picture.

These set of people would expect that the love partner they find must be perfect, never default of positive characters and always willing to give them maximum attention. Because they do not feel themselves to be truly worthy, their happiness then depends on their partner. They feel so insecure about themselves that they would want their partner to make declarations of love to them constantly. However, because of their insecurities they would hardly be truly happy and contented with their love relationships.

In a tantra journey, one first must create a sense of wholeness within the self. You must understand that being single does not mean you are not complete. There is no such thing as a better half. You are your better half so fall in love with yourself!!! Look at yourself in the mirror and appreciate all the qualities that you have both internal and external. Learn to get absorbed in yourself. Take yourself out on a treat, as you would normally have done if you had gone out with a date. Look pretty or charming for yourself. You do not have to wait for someone to tell you that you look good before you tell yourself. When we truly love ourselves, we become happy from within. Remember, you are that special someone and the more you practice loving yourself the more you create a loving atmosphere around yourself. Build yourself up!!! Stop thinking constantly of that "imaginary love partner", instead get absorbed in your world.

Engage yourself totally on the things that you love doing, who knows, someone might be around the corner secretly admiring you while you are enjoying those activities that you are doing. So many people are often attracted to those who surround themselves with the things they love.

Remember, a tantra relationship should often emphasize on a deep level of emotional and spiritual connection and if you are not able to sort yourself out first, then not only would you become emotionally unstable, but you would not also truly connect with a partner.

Let the Hunting Begin

Since Tantra is mostly about making a spiritual connection with another, the hunt for the soulmate should be something " more flowery, respectful, honoring" and not just some sort of "hook up". Tantra deals with conscious loving, so one must be deliberate in the actions towards another. Meaning that you must be interested in really studying and knowing that person. You must understand that in any kind of love relationship, friendship is key. You need to develop a deep trusting and intimate friendship towards that person. It is this friendship that ignites a spiritual connection leading to the heightening of the sexual energy between you and your potential tantra mate.

Understand that some sort of " flirting" must first take place before a connection is made. In making your move towards that potential mate, you must be patient and to learn how to take your time. As a guy, you must understand that when you flirt you do not do it to feel good about yourself. You are trying to make a friend out of that person and not to make a score. Mind your behavior, most tantra partners want a nice guy and not someone who is trying to prove that they are not just cool, but also a "bad ass. In the tantra path, we must be careful and respectful when it comes to other people's boundaries.

These things should be done by will, you cannot assert your demands on the person you are flirting with. For instance, a man could ask outrightly what a woman wants. He should try to ask her about the day and time that going out on a date would be convenient for her. He could also ask her of the time it would be okay for him to call her. These things should be done ever so carefully and consciously. But then one other thing that should be noted when flirting with someone is that we should not try to act like someone we are not. Remember that it is who we are that matters and not what we are.

How Can You Detect the Right Person For You?

Tantra deals with spiritual attraction this means that one must look beyond the physical qualities of a potential partner. One way or the other we all imagine our perfect soulmate to be someone of very intense physical attraction. Most ladies would always dream about that very tall, dark and handsome guy with piercing and intimidating eyes, however as time goes on and with a clearer understanding of tantra, the whole idea of the "perfect mate" completely changes. The basic aim of tantra is to look beyond the physical being to see and connect with the inner soul of the "potential love partner".

You must erase all forms of stereotypes of how you want the ideal partner to be. Forget about the country the person might have come from, forget about the race, age, religion and culture and focus on the inner qualities of that individual. Do not join the " group " that always talk about having a "Type" when it comes to love partners. Looking beyond the physical one can find new and unlimited number of loves matches. Yes, aiming for the eyes works. In practicing tantra you must look into the eyes of the potential love partner to see the god/goddess within. This is because tantra practice believes that every person is a divine being with a divine nature and so should be viewed and treated as such.

In searching for the Tantra mate, you must look deeply within the mind as to how you want that person to be. Ask yourself if you value physical qualities over the inner one. When you meet a potential tantra mate ask yourself, "is the person nice?", is he or she one who would put your thoughts and wellbeing first? Do you think he or she can take very good care of you?

But also, apart from looking beyond their eyes, other factors could determine in detecting the right tantra partner. The main issue is, "Do both of you agree on basic things that could make the relationship work? How committed do you want to get to that relationship? What are your contributions to making that relationship to work? The basic rule is that you can make " any" relationship to work if you want it to work, that is, if you set your mind at it no matter the obstacle that comes your way. If you both are committed to getting along and you have enough love and respect for each other to work out any differences, then there is almost nothing that could stop the relationship from not working out.

Preparing For A Fresh Start With A Tantric Partner

Before you enter a new relationship, you have to clear up your conflicts with your past relationship. The mind is a very strong factor in almost every aspect of our lives and until we have fully cleared and prepared our minds against all doubts, one cannot be fully ready for a new relationship. There are some things that some people believe in their minds about love and whether they admit it or not these people unconsciously sabotage their efforts of entering a new relationship. Are you amongst these set of people? What are the things that you believe about love that is hindering you from entering a new relationship? What kind of beliefs do you have about finding a Tantric Match? Now let us explore some of these beliefs.

One of the most common reasons why some people feel easily depressed and insecure when they think about relationships is because of the belief that even if they find someone, the love will soon turn sour. This is not always true. Some people think that love does not always last forever. However, one must change the mind against these beliefs. Tantra teaches about conscious and deliberate loving. With deliberate steps through tantra one can

44

learn how to love another. You must understand that love should not depend on your feelings. If you set your mind at constantly loving someone, you would.

"Being in love is miserable. It makes one weak. It makes one vulnerable. Love distracts one from his/her focus in life". This not always have to be true. In fact, with the right tantric partner, this is not true at all. Your partner could become your greatest pillar of support. True love makes one stronger and not weak. Love produces happiness and when you are happy with yourself and your tantric partner then you should never feel miserable. One of the biggest believe and fear that people carry around regarding relationships is that having sex with your partner can ruin your relationship. Understand that love is not based on sex. Your values and your worth should not be determined by your body at all. A true tantric partner understands that a spiritual and emotional connection is the goal and not just the consummation of the physical body. But then the belief that sex destroys a relationship could affect a person's thoughts actions and behaviors that would then lead to the breakup of that relationship.

Benefits of Tantric sex

Tantric sex is a moderate type of closeness that may build closeness and a mind-body association that regularly causes solid climaxes. This blend of having a solid body, brain, and soul association, alongside various, amazing sexual climaxes, will have cherishing couples invigorated by expanding the emission of the pineal and pituitary organs.

Sexual Health Improves

Some case that tantric sex has a restoring impact, improving people sexual wellbeing. Visit climaxes, as one of the cerebrum wave reenactments, may change body science. Sorrow and stress may vanish. A lady's sexual wellbeing might be incredibly improved.

For instance, an examination done by Wilkes University found that creation love in any event two times every week discharges a counter acting agent considered immunoglobulin An or IgA, which may shield the body from ailment.

Climaxes Strengthen Immune System

Climaxes may help ease gloom and make you look and feel more youthful. Some trust it can likewise draw out your lifespan, reinforce the safe framework, and improve in general wellbeing.

Potential Benefits of Frequent Orgasms, Tantric Sex, and Women's Health

Visit climaxes may profit a lady's sexual wellbeing. Be that as it may, there is an immense difference between a customary climax and a tantric climax. Normal climaxes last a brief length and stay confined in the sexual organs. Tantric sex climaxes hypothetically include the full body, personality, and soul, and keep going for a considerable length of time.

As per antiquated practices, to get the advantages of a tantric climax, the shakti or vitality, and the rising kundalini, must puncture each of the chakras (vortexes of vitality in the unobtrusive body) as it rises the spinal string. It must arrive at the mind's focal sensory system and endocrine war room—the nerve center and pituitary organ, which directions the progressions that advantage our sexual wellbeing.

Aficionados of tantric sex accept that visit, amazing climaxes increment the degree of the climax hormone, oxytocin. They additionally accept oxytocin levels and your climaxes influence your states of mind, energy, social aptitudes, and feelings, all of which may impact different parts of your day by day life.

Tantric sex depends on a way of thinking of oriental root that is in excess of 4 thousand years of age, utilizing sexual vitality to accomplish an association between bodies, without accomplishing a sexual relationship under the standards thought about ordinary by the Western culture.

This method depends on Tantra, identified with a sort of sexual move, which must be adjusted to the cadence of each couple or traditions, continually targeting accomplishing a glad sexual life, through the ease of constructive vitality inside every individual.

To do this sexual practice, a progression of statutes controlled by the Eastern culture must be connected, with some outside impacts that will make this a life-changing background.

The principal reason to apply is to live at the time, attempt to stay away from a wide range of diversions, which implies that during the demonstration, both must be available with brain and body to appreciate the demonstration to the most extreme.

At that point, you should acknowledge your accomplice as he/she is, without seeing physical or mental shortcomings so that you can take the relationship in full, and not just one must acknowledge the body of an individual, yet additionally the body itself, with any defects it may have.

A significant point in tantric sex is the planning of the earth where the connection will occur, so you should consider the air, light, scents, sustenance and atmosphere, this will guarantee that the energies stream in an unbelievable manner between the two individuals.

In this sexual practice, individuals should do not hesitate to state what they think or need to do with their accomplice, on the grounds that there ought to be no hindrances, however a private correspondence between both.

The objective with tantric sex as in other sexual strategies will consistently be to arrive at the best delight conceivable, it is prescribed to keep eye to eye connection with your accomplice for an additional power and genuinely staggering climaxes.

In this sort of eccentric practices, one must stay cool and know about the passionate and sensorial sensations, for example, contact, vision, smell and hearing at each piece of your accomplice's body, this will produce another world brimming with conceivable outcomes for delight.

As per specialists, when performing tantric sex, individuals significantly improve their physical wellbeing, because of the measure of calories that are lost in this training, which straightforwardly impacts the breath, the heartbeat and blood course.

A few examinations likewise demonstrate that a great many people experience serious phases of despondency, yet in addition state that couples who take part in tantric sex, have improved extensively from this with the disposal of pessimistic vitality and fascination of constructive ones.

To do this training, the couple must consent to do as such, with the sole target to accomplish life-changing climaxes.

Dedicating yourself to any training must have settlements. There are numerous profits from putting time and vitality into tantric sex. Tantric sex practices can enable you to accomplish the accompanying:

1. Draw out delight. Tantric sex strategies make lovemaking—including the glimmer—keep going quite a while. This happens through ejaculatory control as well as by figuring out how to coordinate sexual vitality anyplace in the body or into profound manifestations.

2. Enable ladies. Numerous ladies experience the ill effects of low confidence. They may have a poor self-perception, or they may surrender to sex when they would truly like to say no or not tell their accomplice what they truly need. In tantric sex, ladies are treated with the regard and respect they want and merit.

3. Extend your conceivable outcomes for adoration. Tantric sex tells you the best way to develop the physical and

otherworldly association with your accomplice, and support and love yourself.

4. Help you accomplish genuine fulfillment from sex. When the sex demonstration is finished, are you ever left with the inclination that you are not so much wrapped up? This is regularly because the sexual act does not go past the private parts—it does not contact the heart. In tantric sex, you can arrive at the state where each cell in your body feels supported from the spirit association you feel with your accomplice. At the point when sex occurs with this sort of heart association, both body and psyche are nourished.

5. Enable men. Such a significant number of men stress over their penis size, and to what extent they last in sex. Numerous additionally do not have a clue how to submit or please a lady.

6. At the point when men feel progressively enabled in sex, they become increasingly certain and open to be all the more minding in their relationship.

7. Ease nerves and wretchedness. Measurements show a huge number of people experience the ill effects of uneasiness and melancholy, including manifestations like weariness, listlessness, and resting and eating aggravations. Tantric sex gives a colossal wellspring of

vitality to the body and tranquility to the mind that conquers these issues.

8. Influence the world decidedly. Your own additions cause you to create more positive and adoring vitality ostensibly, stretching out to everybody you meet, modifying the vitality of the planet since everything on a mystical or otherworldly level are interrelated.

9. Raise sex. When you hoist sex to a degree of holiness, it takes on a more extravagant measurement than an insignificant physical act.

10. Tap into the wellspring of youth. For all the medical advantages referenced beforehand, rehearsing tantra can make you feel and look youthful once more.

11. Recuperate past enthusiastic injuries. Tantric sex can enable you to mend past damages from a wide range of difficult or horrendous encounters in which you felt double-crossed or abused. Instead, it encourages you make encounters of being regarded and regarded in sex and in life as a rule.

12. Revive your wellbeing. Rehearsing tantric sex has physiological and mental impacts that keep up—and recover—wellbeing. For instance, breathing systems carry more air into the body, supporting the tissues and muscles. Research has demonstrated a connection between the

52

impacts of unwinding, contemplation, and otherworldliness and better physical and passionate wellbeing. Individuals who are otherworldly have lower circulatory strain, lower levels of uneasiness and sadness, progressively stable hormone levels, and better working invulnerable frameworks.

13. Extend your association with others. Tantric sex gives more significance to life and enhances your connections.

Advantages and Disadvantages with Traditional Sex

Tantric sex and our regular "sexual" sex are very different, and in some ways, people don't even realize the impact of tantric sex, and how it can change the way you have sex.

A Different Pathway

Regular sex has three different stages: foreplay, the act of intercourse, and of course the climax or ending. Once that is done, it actually is the end, and usually, you're done. Sometimes you have sex and you go back to your normal life.

But tantric sex is different. Tantric sex has zero linear progression. You might not even have an orgasm until after foreplay and intercourse, or maybe even just foreplay brings you to that level. The idea behind it is not to just focus on the orgasm, and don't use the orgasm as the ending point.

The Energies that are There

The energy that is in a regular bout of sex is different. It is purely sexual, penis or vagina against another genitalia, and the whole act is physical. Whether it be kissing, rubbing, pinching, or even penetration he idea behind it is physical, and not as mental. Oftentimes, people might not even look at one another, and it is something that you need to realize makes tantric sex a little different.

The connection that is there during tantric sex isn't just a physical manifestation, but it's also a different type of manifestation of energy. This is more than just sexual energy, but they try to expand that energy from the genitalia out to the rest of the body so that it can cause pleasure in different forms.

Working Together

The thing with regular sex is, usually the endgame of it is an orgasm, to have that release, and then you are done. You are more focused on that than just working and experiencing the moment together.

The crazy thing about tantric sex is you can have an orgasm not just from the act of intercourse alone. Some people have an orgasm from massages, from light foreplay, even pinching or biting the nipples can result in a tantric orgasm. The idea of it is to stop worrying so much about orgasms, and instead, focus on the moment.

You want to make sure that your breathing is like your partner's, and it isn't out of sorts, and it isn't labored or wavering. You also want to keep eye contact with one another.

This is something that most people do not realize they do not do when they engage in regular sex. Whether it be doggy style or even just turning the lights off instead of on, people are scared to look at one another. Maybe it is the vulnerability of the moment, but it actually can change the way it makes you feel. Tantric sex brings you out of the "only me" mindset during sex, making you more selfless, and helping you attain that connection over time.

Time Spent

The time spent during sex usually varies, but most people usually do not spend more than an hour together in the bedroom, unless of course, they want to go long. Sometimes, the quickie sessions last all but five minutes, and that is it. But here is the thing, tantric sex can last a long time, several hours at that.

That is partially because they aren't trying to do this just to get off, but instead, they want to submerge into a way where they can cyclically go together and experience intercourse. The crazy thing about this is that tantric sex causes more orgasms and more powerful orgasms than standard sex does.

The end of the game is not a depletion of the physical energies, but instead, you're both experiencing a cyclical direction of you both experiencing the fun and pleasure of one another, and the pleasure and intensity spent.

The Touching

The limitation of regular sex is that it focuses mostly on physical touch and it does not work on a higher plane than that. But, the crazy thing about tantric sex, is that they may not touch one another in some cases. Sometimes, people might just barely move their hands there, and sometimes, they feel an increased series of pleasure.

It also causes orgasm waves as well. This is because tantric sex is not just a small little wave of pleasure, but instead a deeper, almost mesmerizing wave of pleasure that comes from the orgasm that's there too. It is amazing how this can change the way that you feel, and the pleasure and fire that goes through this.

Tantric sex does not always involve a bunch of touching, nor does it have to involve extreme pain or anything that's here. Instead, it can be a wave of orgasms that are different, and powerful as well.

The wild thing about tantric sex is that it involves a pure and mesmerizing form of energy with one another, and it helps to develop and broaden your ability to experience pleasure.

The Strongest Energy

Some people think tantric sex is not the strongest form of energy, but it is. That is because it's a human connection directly through energy, and with physical sex, sure you're touching, but sometimes the full-on connection isn't like that. Tantric sex is to regular sex what yoga is to your average gym workout. Both are great, but the thing is, if you want a deeper connection physically and mentally with your partner, you oftentimes will feel it within the body through tantric sex, rather than just through your average bout in the bedroom.

Tantric sex spreads through the entire body, and it permeates through, almost like a sponge soaking up all that energy and then releasing it outwards.

Tantric sex is a way for you to manifest the spirit, and in some ways, that's why people argue that tantric sex is the most powerful form of sex, because it involves the spirit, through the action of making love. It is a form of intimacy that's very valid and has many different principles that are incredibly valid, and worth mentioning.

Tantric sex is the better form of sex for that reason alone. It promotes a deeper, more worthwhile connection with the person you love.

With tantric sex, you can get closer and closer to divinity, and you can experience the masterpiece of it. It is a more spiritual, more rewarding and close sex that allows you to experience the divinity. Tantric sex is a wonderful way to really bring you closer to your partner.

Stimulates a Better Relationship

People do not realize that just because you have sex doesn't mean it's meaningful to your partner. Sometimes, you have sex to get off, or to experience pleasure, but you do not really experience the fun and deep connection of a relationship with your partner if you're just having regular sex.

Sure, regular sex is fun for some people, and it can bring about a deep, rewarding connection, but the problem is, oftentimes it creates a bit of a hollow relationship with your partner. Some people just have sex to keep the relationship going, but tantric sex is not about that.

Not all sex is done with the idea of building a connection in mind. Sometimes it is done to just orgasm and that's it. But tantric sex lets you foster a better, deeper connection with your partner, and allows you to have empowered sexuality via arousal and stimulating the senses. You start to experience a comeback of the deepen erotic nature of the senses of sex, and many people realize it creates a more aligned, meaningful experience with your partner.

Many people love this form of sex because it helps bring a more meaningful way to love another human being. Humans want to show to their partner how much they love them, and the thing with tantra is that allows you to really feel the romance, and really spice things up.

You want to bring new things to the table, and tantric sex lets you do that.

Romance is not dead; it's just you get hung up by routines. Tantra is a way for you to keep sex alive and well in your life. And you do not even need to believe in antra to do it. If you want to practice the positions and the fun of it, then you can easily do so through the power of sex.

For most people, the do not realize how their relationship has changed, and they might not realize they even pay attention to your partners. But, with tantric sex, you will be able to really foster a better, deeper connection with the person that you love, and bring forth a better, more reliable connection with yourself, and with your partner as well.

Is Tantric Sex Better?

Now that is not to say you shouldn't ever have regular sex again. You should have sex how you want to have sex, but you should understand that tantric sex stimulates your entire body and forces you to move into a state of vulnerability and wellness. For many people, tantric sex depends on the connection and the love that you share with your partner. If you have ever been curious about tantric sex, it can only help you.

But, the thing with tantric sex, is that it is very long.it takes a long time since there is no end goal. If you want to have normal sex with your partner, then go for it, but understand that it may not have as deep of a connection.

Does tantric sex save relationships? Perhaps, but also understand that sex won't fix everything about a relationship, and if it's already a sinking ship, then you may want to figure out other alternatives and means to really help you get the most out of your sexual relationship. For many, tantric sex builds it all, and makes it so that you are able to build and foster that connection with people that you love. The one that you love matters a lot, and that is why many people enjoy the fun of tantric. It is because, it isn't just the sex act itself, but also the act of being connected with the person around you, and the one that you love.

Now that you understand that, you will see how tantra betters the full spirit, whereas regular sex I mostly a physical affair. Both are wonderful to experience, but if you feel like fostering a deeper, more meaningful connection with the person that you love, tantra is the name of the game and its key for that.

That is why many people love tantra because it allows for you to foster that love and understanding with the one that you're with. It can improve your health, wellness, and happiness too.

So, which is best? The answer is tantra, but it is also important to understand the differences. Both of them do have their pros and cons, and you'll understand that, with each moment and each experience you share with your partner, there are a lot of benefits to be had with this and a lot that you certainly should try to enjoy.

Identify and Worship the God or Goddess Within You

Most people follow the path of Tantra to approach God. God has blessed every aspect of your life; this applies to sex as well. You will be able to connect with God and the divinity, only when you are making love to your partner, since this is the only way in which you are respecting as well as experiencing the divinity that resides within the human body. The teaching of Tantra firmly states that there lies a God in every man and a Goddess in every woman. This implies that your body is the vessel for divinity. For attaining the significant levels of wisdom that are accessible to you, you will simply have to let go of this shell. Your self-esteem will improve when your partner is honoring you, and you are honoring them in return. Only when you can see this aspect of yourself, only then will you be able to see the divinity that lives in others as well clearly.

In this portion, you will learn and identify the divinity that lives within you. You will be able to identify the God and Goddess within your body and that of your partner as well. This forms the essence of Tantric sex. You will also be able to start to become more enlightened. This segment covers information about different Gods and Goddesses that are popular in Tantric teachings.

The Terms 'God' and 'Goddess'

As mentioned, the teachings of Tantra state that every man and woman should be treated like a God or a Goddess. This is to make sure that you not only think of yourself as a vessel for divinity but treat your partner with the same regard as well. In this manner, you will be able to respect and honor your partner in the manner that you are supposed to. This will also ensure that you can honor the power that exists within the universe.

The different deities usually worshiped in Tantric sex are beings filled with light. They symbolize various energies as well as relationships. The other terms that are usually used for gods and goddesses are Deva and Devi, priest and priestess, and Daka and Dakini respectively. These deities are believed to possess power and wisdom. This power of theirs can also be projected within your body. This projection simply depends on the various virtues and qualities that you possess.

Goddess is a term that has repeatedly been used in Tantra. It is made use of for describing a woman who is in touch with the feminine power that resides within her body. The initial meaning of this word usually meant a woman who was nurturing and strong. A man is not referred to as God because God is considered to be a superior being in various religions. There are some religions and even a few practices that believe that a person can become a god or a goddess by changing a few aspects of themselves. However, the teachings of Tantric sex state that a person has a certain level of divinity that is present within them since birth and nothing can be done to change this.

Tantric sex rules state that regardless of race, religion or even caste of the person, there is some divinity present in everyone. By referring to a woman as a goddess, you are simply honoring her feminine characteristics that make her a lover, a hunter, seductress and nurturing individual. Only when a woman comes to terms with her characteristics and accepts herself for who she is, will she be able to honor herself and be honored by those around her. By addressing a man as a god, you are simply honoring his basic characteristics of being a protector, healer, provider and a symbol of power. He will need to accept these characteristics that exist within him and only then can his partner honor him. You might be aware of these characteristics, or they might simply be present within you, and you have not discovered them yet.

Identify your Roles and Characteristics

When you are getting started with the journey towards Tantric sex, then the first thing that you will need to do is identify the gods or the goddesses that define you. For doing this, you will need to identify your basic characteristics and the different roles that you play in your life. Do you consider yourself to be beautiful? Are you intelligent? Are you an entrepreneur? Are you powerful? And so on, and so forth. You can write down all your answers to such questions. For making things easier for yourself, you can create a collage, or you can use mind-mapping as well. Place a picture of yourself in the center of a sheet and then start writing about all the characteristics that you think you possess.

Once you have gathered information about the various gods and goddesses that has been provided in the latter part, you can list down the names of deities that you associate yourself. For instance, if you have written that you are powerful, then perhaps you can relate yourself to Shiva or even Ares. If you think you are beautiful, then you can write down the name of Aphrodite.

Look beyond the superficial layer

You probably will have heard the phrase "never judge a book by its cover." Everyone has probably heard this phrase at one point in time or another. We tend to judge a person solely based on their looks, the way they dress, or even the job that they do. You might have made statements like "she is too skinny," or "he is too short." You probably looked at a person's bank account before agreeing to go out on a date with him. However, Tantra deals with an individual's persona and not their superficial characteristics. There are three basic steps that you will need to follow to worship the divinity that exists within your partner.

The first step would be to accept that there is divinity that exists within you. The second step is to embrace and identify the divinity that exists within your partner as well. You will need to strike a balance between the masculine and the feminine energies of the deities. The third step would be to unite these deities within you, through your union with your partner. This will help in creating the much-needed balance between the two and help you attain a greater level of ecstasy.

Why is it important to worship each other?
Every person is happier when they know that they are being acknowledged. It feels great when you are appreciated by those who are around you. Do you know how you feel when someone notices you? When someone tries to understand you? Tantric sex is all about worshiping yourself and your partner as well. This does not mean that you will have to worship each other blindly. It simply means that you both need to shower each other with unconditional love. Unconditional love does not mean unconditional power over one another. It simply means that serving each other to the best of your abilities to attain mutual pleasure.

When you start following the path of Tantric sex, you will find that it feels good to hear positive things about yourself and you will also want to keep complimenting your partner. This is the meaning of being worshiped and worshipping your partner.

Learning About the Gods and Goddesses

There are different male and female gods as well as goddesses found in different cultures around the world like Egyptian, Greek, Roman and Indian as well. These gods and goddesses are mostly from an ancient era. Let us learn more about the different goddesses.

Most of the goddesses often represent fertility and life. However, they are also seen as seductresses who seduce their partners and engage in sexual intercourse with them. In this portion, you will read about a few main goddesses, and you can perhaps find a few traits that you associate yourself with.

Aphrodite:
Aphrodite is considered to be the most famous of Greek goddesses. She represents beauty, desire, love and sexuality. She also represents friendship. Aphrodite is often represented by doves, roses, puppies and even dolphins as well. According to Roman mythology, she is referred to as Venus. In Roman mythology, she is the symbol of purity.

Artemis:
She is considered to be the Goddess of hunting. Artemis is a Greek goddess, and she represents the moon and is a virgin goddess. She is a warrior and a hunter, the female counterpart to complement Ares, the God of war.

Athena:
The goddess of wisdom and knowledge. She is the patron goddess of Athens. Strategy and planning are the two traits that are commonly associated with Athena.

Juno:

Juno or Hera, depending upon whether it is the Greek or Roman version of mythology is considered to be a mother like figure with a nurturing and a calming nature.

Hindu Goddesses

There are various goddesses in India and Nepal, and each of them has been given a lot of importance. Various ceremonies are conducted to honor each of these goddesses. The main goddesses are mentioned here.

Durga is considered to be the mother of all goddesses. Tara is considered to represent wisdom as well as kindness. Lakshmi is the goddess of wealth and prosperity. Saraswati is the goddess of various art forms and skill. Kali represents strength and power. She is also the protector of the realm.

Gods from Different Cultures

Every religion has different gods and goddesses. These gods often have a counterpart in the form of a goddess. There are different deities worshiped by different cultures. They all represent immense strength, power, and are often thought of as super beings. This part covers carious gods from different religions. You might be able to identify your traits or those of your partner in this list given here.

Hindu gods include Lord Shiva who has got immense power and Lord Vishnu is considered to be the God of all Gods. There are different manifestations of Lord Shiva, and there are quite a few representations of his dark side as well. Shakti is the consort of Lord Shiva. Lord Shiva and Shakti form a powerful pair and represent pure energy. Ganesh is a very popular god as well; he is a young boy with the head of an elephant. Lord Ganesh is known to remove obstacles and spread happiness. Lord Rama and Sita form a couple that is often worshiped all over India, they are considered to be the perfect couple and represent the harmony that should exist between a husband and wife.

Greek Gods

There are numerous Greek gods, and they have all become famous because of the strength and power that they hold. Zeus is considered to be the greatest of all; he is the King of all gods and the supremely powerful Alpha-male. Eros is commonly referred to, as Cupid, and he is cherub or a little boy who is often mischievous and often keeps shooting arrows of love at people around him. He is the God of love. Dionysus is the Greek and the Roman god of lust. According to the legends, he always chased women and indulged in drinking a lot of wine. He indeed is the god of lust.

Preparing for Tantric Sex: The Things Most Important

The Correct Mindset

Balance into your space after a bath and adhere honorably to the rites of the area and calm the mind to grant permission for energies mixing. Sit up with doing the eye gazing and breathing techniques. Say a chant to align your energy while calming the mind.

Talk to your Partner

It's so normal in the average sex life of a couple that they just go into the sexual action quietly. But tantric sex says no to sex this way since it is practice of dedication and not an unconscious action. Take time to sit opposite each other and plan your actions during lovemaking together. The energy of sex and love is a powerfully driven energy. Open up on what you would love to show or carry out during love making and it will very much likely happen as you allow energy to expand and blend. In turns, pour out your heart on the matter allowing your every need come up. Freely ask of your partner what you need.

Prepare the Place

The Perfect Romance Set
Picture a movie setting for the most romantic movie ever imagined. How does this set look like in your mind? Have you

ever wondered if you and your partner share the same picturesque of an ideal lovemaking space? It's essential you discuss your different ideas on a perfect set for lovemaking.

Build your Set Aside Lovemaking Area

Picture one of the classiest cathedrals you have ever been in. Think of replicating the classy nature in your lovemaking area, preparing the area meticulously.

Dressing your lovemaking area is so similar to dressing up yourself in many ways. Just as you dressed up in nice outfits, dress your room to its best. You could follow these tips:

- Lit the whole room with candles strategically positioned.

- Add a nice different scent to the room without going overboard probably with some fresh flowers or Aromatic room oils.

- Get a new bed covering and dress you bed beautifully.

- Get massage oils. They will likely come in handy at one point

- Get your bed taste buds stimulants which could include chocolate coated strawberry or chilled champagne.

- Clear every mess and put everything in their right places to avoid the area looking messy.

Tilt your Set

Try to be expressively creative when making love. Make love at a variety of places, indoors or outdoors. Things will fall into place beautifully when you bond together with a blessed intention and spiritual union.

But it's still a pretty good idea sticking to your same lovemaking set as it heightens the energy build up and enhances your union once you in that area.

The Right Music Choice

Certain type of songs strikes a chord and penetrates the soul. Researchers have confirmed specific sounds, beats and tempo play a large role in dictating our breathing pattern and heart rate. It becomes more lucid that music is an essential on a tantric date. Make the right music choice and watch as you and lover bask in the moment with enjoyment, it could be classical, R n B or Hip Hop. Your music selection should be solely determined by the mood set you wish to trigger

The Altar Construction

An altar is a designated space crafted out to keep what you hold dear and sacred; it could also be a representative symbol for prayers. Get sacred objects you cherish, which inspire you to higher levels of consciousness. Decorate the house with those sacred objects to give it a spiritual feel when you take a look at them. These decorations should be done collectively with your partner, it is a bonding experience.

Before making love, you both approach the altar to say a word of prayer in silence or aloud. The items on your altar could include your pictures or that of your respected leaders, candles, water, air, flowers or sacred objects.

Prepare the Body

• Always ensure your fingernails clean and neatly cut. Neatly trimmed clean nails are attractive (Dirty nails are turnoffs for both sexes) and essential for maintaining a good hygiene because your fingers sometimes serve as simulators on your partner skin or to pleasure her organs.

• Brush your teeth daily, particularly before a romantic time with your partner. Like nails an unbrushed teeth are the toppers on the list of turnoffs for men and women. Utilize a baking soda inclusive toothpaste for really good cleansing and a nice mouthwash for that extra bit of freshness.

• Wash each other's hair. Particularly when a man does it to his woman, as it is a rarely seen action.

• Shave her, paying special attention to being soft on her skin. Putting trust in him to carry this out will make him feel proud and pleased. The woman should also do same for her man.

• Do his nails. Paint her toenails too.

- Modify the bathroom lighting. Most bathrooms have harsh lighting. Replace the bulbs with really nice colored ones for special evenings that creates a whole new sensual world.

- Prepare a bath for each other in turns or stir up the romantic universe by sharing a bath together. A cool bath is stimulating but it's best going for warm water as it comes highly recommended for relaxation and generating warm feelings. So, ensure you check the water temperature.

- Buy and use specially scented soaps, bathing oils and soft brushes. Most supermarkets have segregated portions for bath items. Go out and get the best for you with your partner in mind also.

- Set up an exit with a mat, a cozy bathrobe and large soft towel. Isolate the latter two items from whatever you use daily to make the experience special.

Which Massages to Use

Compression - This is where you use two hands, palms down to apply pressure on certain areas of the body. This causes the blood to flow to that area and the muscles relax in a big way. This massage technique is best performed on expansive areas of the body like the shoulders and the back.

The stroking technique – It is very easy to perform this one. You just need to use the whole of your palm and give long strokes while at the same time applying gentle but firm pressure on the muscles. It is very rewarding, and she will love you for it. You can use the long strokes on every area of her lovely body; say, you could even use it from the toes to the hips, from the neck to the buttocks and so on. Keep your fingers straight, even the thumb. She will love this.

Using the friction method – This is also a common method that you can use on a woman. It involves firm rubbing on the fingers and the palms against a part of the body. It does not need you to use oils, but then you should be a bit gentle with the skin of your lover. Experts say that this is an advanced technique, but you can perfect it with enough practice.

Kneading – You can perform this just the same way that you would knead dough. It is easy and it is recommended for the fleshy parts like the buttocks. You will have to get hold of the muscles between the thumb and the other fingers and lift gently, let go, repeat the same, press and so on. It is very relaxing, a good way to connect two lovers.

Massaging the legs – The legs are part and parcel of the Tantra massage because they are very sensitive. You should start with the long stroking massage and then caress them with the tips of your fingers. Good leg massage is best given when she is lying on her stomach.

Buttocks massage – This important body part should never be missed out in any Tantra massage book. You should proceed from the legs to the buttocks, a very erotic part of the body. This is part of, or a prelude to foreplay. As we said before, kneading and stroking are perfect techniques for this part. However, since the buttocks are fleshy, you require no kneading expertise.

Diet Tips

For having good sex that is satisfying you need to have a good flow both through your blood vessels and through your sex organs. You need to satisfy your sex fantasies, so eat well. Foods that increase the flow of blood, testosterone and estrogen are available from our grocery shop. Eating these types of fruits and vegetables will keep you in fit condition always. Your sexual intercourse will be vigorous and satisfying. Here are some of these "sexy foods".

Chocolate

Chocolate dates back a long way in history to the times of Casanova and Louise the XV in terms of being used for stimulating the passions. However, this is applicable only to dark chocolate or at the least containing 70% or more of dark chocolate. The magic ingredient in chocolate that helps boost your senses is phenyl ethylamine. Keep a few pieces in the back of the cupboard for those times when you are feeling low.

Horseradish

This food item is quite popular in Japan. People eat it with their sushi and this side dish packs a wallop in the excitation department. Check out the items in your nearest mall, you might get lucky.

Chili Peppers

This spice helps boost the metabolic rate, meaning it gets the blood flowing. This supposedly triggers the release of endorphins that puts you 'in the mood'.

Oysters

Famous since the olden ages as an aphrodisiac, oysters have zinc in them that is beneficial for the production of testosterone. This increases the sex drive in both men and women. Women get easily "into the mood" when they have oysters.

Nuts

Pine nuts help your libido. They are good for your brain too. Nuts like almonds have plenty of essential amino acids that help to keep sex hormones thriving. Brazil nuts will benefit men more because the selenium content will keep the health of the sperm cells intact.

Caviar

Caviar is fish eggs that have plenty of vitamins. Many people have a sex fantasy that involves caviar. It has phosphorus that makes your nerves steady and active. The best combination for caviar is vodka. But do not drink too much vodka, only a little, or you may have trouble maintaining an erection.

Avocado

Since the time of the Aztecs, avocados have been accepted as one major fruit that increases a person's totalistic energy. The very shape of the fruit is sensuous and delicious; over the past few years, scientists have been studying how much of an aphrodisiac the fruit actually is. Despite the fact the research is still being conducted, the fact remains that avocado contains high levels of Vitamin E and helps you retain an energy level that is unprecedented.

Honey

The very idea of honey is something that sparks a sensuous image in our heads; not for nothing do we call sex 'the birds and the bees'. It has long since served as a symbol of procreation in literature and art, but the fact is adding a few spoons of honey to your daily diet will boost your sex life unimaginably! It contains the nutrient boron, which not only gives you a natural energy boost but also regulates your estrogen and testosterone levels, so use honey creatively in food as well as your lovemaking!

Keys to Tantra

When we talk to people about Tantra, some are surprised. They look at us and say, "Sex for three hours? That is not possible!" Of course, the focus of Tantra is not to have a sex marathon, though that can be achieved. The goal is to forget the barriers that create a 'limit' on sex. Time is one such barrier, where we might constantly be thinking about the time it should take for us to have sex. How long or short should it be?

Another barrier is orgasm itself, as people who seek to achieve it become fixated on it, ignoring the other person and the very act of sex itself.

Tantra takes all the conventional concepts and focus points that we have about sex and replaces them with ideas that truly bring out the best this physical act can offer.

Experience

Tantra is about tapping into the sexual energy that we possess. Through that, we take charge of our physical and emotional forces to open an entirely new dimension of sex.

How does this change occur? One of the main goals of Tantra is to create a heightened level of intimacy with your partner. The sex aspect occurs because you share an emotional connection with your partner, and this link is the force you can use to have sex something truly special. This force is capable of communicating many things, such as love, trust, admiration, and even respect. Through the act of sex, you are able to convey a range of emotions.

But what about the physical force? Where does that come in? When you have sex without emotions, then it just becomes an act of satisfying your desires and urges. With Tantra, sex becomes something extraordinary. It becomes a physical force.

You now have the emotional force and physical force working in total harmony – just like the yin and the yang. Tantra allows you to experience pleasure, love, and a more peaceful state of mind.

Intimacy

Through Tantric sexual experiences, you can create a deeper and truer connection with your partner. You develop a level of intimacy that fosters trust, understanding, and love.

Gentleness

There is a sense of tenderness to Tantra that speaks volumes of the sexual act in which you and your partner are engaged. This gentleness communicates respect, longing, and admiration. It allows you and your partner to appreciate each other to the fullest.

Slow

Sex is not rushed. Tantra dials down the speed of foreplay and intercourse. You become aware of the act and recognize each move you are making. You are truly grasping sensations, whether they are emotional or physical. At the same time, you gain a newfound admiration and respect for your body, as well as that of your partner.

Presence

Tantra wants you to experience the joys of sex. What had happened yesterday does not concern you now. What could happen in the future is best left to ponder at another time. All that matters in the present is what you and your partner are indulging in.

Sensuality

Allowing yourself and your partner to feel sensual before you become sexual lets you communicate sensations between your mind, body, and soul. At the same time, you can enjoy a prolonged sexual experience and delay ejaculation as much as possible. All the techniques that Tantra mentions about meditation, exercises, touch, and foreplay are there to help you enter into a state that is known as a "sexual meditation." In other words, when you are having sex, it feels like a beautiful and meditative experience. You absorb every feeling and sensation, and that helps you enjoy sex for longer duration.

Ready and Steady Before You Go

Tantra takes a holistic approach to sex. As you are probably aware by now, Tantra isn't about the results, but the journey to get there. Eventually, you might forget what you intended to achieve in the first place – such is the transformative nature of Tantra. Your environment also plays a critical role in determining your mindset, improving your ability to relax and become ready, and keep your breathing and tension steady. Once you have set the mood, you are prepared to go on the journey.

Suggestions to Improve Tantric sex

Temperature

Make sure that your room or space is at a comfortable temperature. If the room is too hot, turn on the air conditioner and set the temperature to the 70s range, which ensures the place is cool, but not chilly. For cold temperatures, turn on the heat at least an hour before you begin to have sex.

Lighting

You can choose to set the mood with either candles or tinted light bulbs. Candles work well to add a touch of romance, while tinted bulbs make the space sensual and erotic. What you choose depends on the kind of atmosphere you would like to create.

Scent

You can also fill the space with a beautiful scent. You can use essential oils, scented candles, flowers, or incense sticks. We recommend avoiding air fresheners and sprays. Sticking to something a bit more natural sets the right mood. Make sure that you pick a scent that you and your partner can both enjoy. You or your partner might be allergic to certain fragrances, so try out different scents so that you can discover if either of you has any allergies you both should be aware of.

Softness

Ensure the surface that you choose for sex is soft. Even if you decide to pick the floor, try to make it more comfortable by placing a soft blanket, cushions, or pillows. If you are on the bed, then decorate it further with cushions.

Vibes

Enhance the sexual and romantic vibe by playing soft music. You might even want to dance to the music before you have sex.

Before We Get to the Fun Part

People often wonder if there is a ritual to perform before starting Tantric sex. There isn't – Tantra isn't nearly so strict as to provide a specifically prescribed method for interacting with your partner. However, we do have some tips to allow your sexual energy to flow freely through your body, build sexual tension, and communicate your lust to your partner. It's a good idea to practice these before your first Tantric sex experience, to ensure you and your partner are on the same page and ready to move forward as you begin this journey together.

Eye of the Beholder

Look into each other's eyes as long as possible without blinking and try to communicate whatever you feel to him or her. Do you suddenly feel awkward? Don't hide those feelings. Bring them out. In fact, many couples have ended up laughing uncontrollably. That is okay, too. You are allowing all the emotions to cascade out of you. Enjoy the moment and let it continue for as long as you like. Tantra is all about slowing down and appreciating each moment you spend together, so don't rush on to the next step – take your time and really see your partner for who they are. And make sure you are allowing your own gaze to reflect your innermost self, as well.

When you look into each other's eyes, you are letting each other know that you would like to enjoy an exciting, pleasurable, and wonderful sexual experience, but you are in no hurry. For now, you are both content admiring each other. You hold each other on a pedestal, and that is what you must convey through your eyes.

Breath of the Wild
Try to synchronize your breathing. You can do this by encouraging your partner to relax. Allow him or her to bring their breathing to a calm state. Once their breathing is regular, you can match it with your own. There is no need to rush through the process.

In many cases, people might find themselves feeling nervous, since what they are about to experience is novel to them. There is a sense of anticipation and excitement. When you and your partner are in the midst of all that excitement, make sure you maintain eye contact. Let each other know how much fun you are having and how much you yearn for each other. Once you have exhausted everything you would like to communicate with each other, focus on calming and synchronizing your breathing.

Touch of the Pleasure

Don't hesitate to tell your partner what you like. When they touch you in a certain way or become playful with you, be open with them about whatever it is you would like them to do. If certain actions sent waves of pleasure through you, let your partner know that they should continue – and let them do the same with you. Find out what really drives your partner wild. Sometimes, you don't even have to use words to say it. You can let your partner know what you like or want more of by doing something to show them your feelings of pleasure. In the same way, communicate to your partner that he or she can feel free to use their own body language to guide your touches to really turn them on.

Mind of the Lover

If you have specific intentions for your sexual experience, then don't be afraid to set them. You are not going to lower the intensity of sex in any way – in fact, determining an intention can help you get closer to your partner. However, don't stick to a certain act. For example, as we have repeated throughout the book, your objective should not be about achieving orgasm. Rather, allow your intention to engulf the entire experience. You could say that you would like to have better sex, which has a far more meaningful outcome for you and your partner – and may or may not include orgasm, specifically. You could also have emotional intentions, such as building the love between yourself and your partner, strengthening trust, or adding more happiness to your relationship. These are all important goals for any couple, and they can be achieved through simply practicing Tantra.

CPSIA information can be obtained
at www.ICGtesting.com
Printed in the USA
LVHW081832300322
714841LV00004B/242